SOLOS FOR JAZZ FLUTE

MW00563948

CLASSIC JAZZ SOLOS AS PLAYED BY:
BUDDY COLLETTE
HERBIE MANN
SAM MOST
ERIC DOLPHY
JAMES MOODY
PAUL HORN
HUBERT LAWS
JOE FARRELL
JEREMY STEIG
JAMES NEWTON
DAVE VALENTIN

ANALYSES AND NOTE-FOR-NOTE
TRANSCRIPTIONS BY
BOB AFIFI

COMPLETE WITH A CATALOG OF
JAZZ PHRASES BY EACH ARTIST

Compilation edited by RONNY S. SCHIFF

CARL FISCHER®
62 Cooper Square, New York, NY 10003

ATJ307   ISBN 0-8258-0414-0

CONTENTS

INTRODUCTION

The flute as lead instrument in jazz is a relatively recent development. Wayman Carver (1905 - 1967) is generally acknowledged as the first jazz flutist and can be heard as early as 1935 playing with Chick Webb's Big Band. Despite the work of Carver and others, the flute didn't catch on as a popular jazz instrument until well into the 1950s, when improvements in amplification finally made it possible for the flute to be played at volume levels equivalent to those of the saxophone and trumpet. Before amplification, a jazz flutist would likely accept the depressing reality that his solo would be buried by the sheer volume of the rhythm section with whom he was playing. Consequently, the instrument tended to be used only when doubled by other flutes or when the music was on the quiet side. With adequate amplification, the jazz flutist could at last be heard and appreciated.

Jazz in the '50s underwent significant stylistic changes, and two styles in particular emerged as well suited for the flute: "cool jazz" and "Latin jazz." Cool jazz contrasted sharply with be-bop primarily because it sought to set a mood that was generally more relaxing. Some performers of the style achieved this softer (or smoother) effect by using orchestral instruments such as French horns, oboes, violins and flutes in combination with the typical jazz instrumentation of rhythm section, saxophones and brass. This association helped to familiarize the public with the sound of the flute, even when the role was incidental.

Latin music, particularly the bossa nova from Brazil, became very popular in the United States in the early '60s as dance music, and the flute (which is an integral part of Latin music) began to receive a dramatic increase in exposure. Jazz musicians, such as flutist Herbie Mann, whose popularity soared during the era, were among the first to embrace the rhythms and harmonies of Latin music. The style has endured over the years and Latin music continues to be both a popular and important part of the jazz idiom.

Following the phenomenal success of Herbie Mann, other jazz flutists such as Frank Wess, James Moody, and Sam Most contributed significantly to the growing respect for the instrument's capabilities and helped to increase its popularity during the 1950s, much as Jean-Pierre Rampal had done for the classical flute following World War II.

The 1960s saw players such as Eric Dolphy, Rahsaan Roland Kirk, and Jeremy Steig emerge as major talents on the flute. Dolphy had an extraordinary technical command of the flute as well as an uncanny ability as an improviser, and his work remains some of the most significant jazz flute playing on record. Kirk and Steig became leading exponents of the technique of overblowing and singing with the flute, attracting even more popularity for the instrument. They demonstrated that the flute could achieve intensity like that of the saxophone when played with this technique.

The success of Hubert Laws in the 1970s marked an important development for jazz flutists. In contrast to Steig or Kirk, Laws, a classically-trained flutist, played with a refined tone. He also possessed a technical command of the instrument on a par with the best classical flutists. Laws was able, unlike the majority of jazz musicians, to fill symphony halls with his accessible hybrid of classical, jazz and popular numbers. His example helped not only to gain respect for the flute, but also to elevate the status of jazz in America to that of concert music. Though the majority of jazz flutists are primarily saxophonists who double on the instrument, Hubert Laws inspired many doublers to take their flute playing more seriously and to seek classical training as a way to improve their technique. In addition, his example motivated many classical flutists to study jazz. Other jazz flutists that were significant players in the 1970s include Joe Farrell and Paul Horn, both of whom enjoyed both critical and popular acclaim.

In the 1980s, players such as Dave Valentin and James Newton continued to expand the territory of the flute. Valentin's affinity for Latin music and popular styles made, and continues to make, an enormous impact on both established and aspiring jazz flutists. Newton, starting in the early 1980s, has dominated the Down Beat polls by huge margins as the No. 1 jazz flutist. He possesses an arsenal of techniques on the flute, and his tone and facility, like those of Hubert Laws, are comparable with those of classical flutists. In addition to his accomplishments as a flutist, Newton has also received critical acclaim for his music and recordings as well.

The transcriptions contained in this book cover a wide range of jazz flute styles. Whenever possible, it is highly recommended that you listen to the original recordings of the transcriptions. After all, the music was first performed and was then transcribed, not the other way around.

- Bob Afifi

Buddy Collette
ROOM WITH SKIES

Buddy Collette was born in Los Angeles on August 6, 1921. As a child, he first studied the piano; later he learned the alto, tenor and baritone saxophones, clarinet and flute while at the Los Angeles Conservatory of Music and California Academy of Music. His early professional experience began in 1942, playing with numerous musicians (including Les Hite) and serving in the Navy as a dance band leader during World War II. After the war, Collette made recordings with a variety of groups such as those led by Lucky Thompson, Benny Carter and Louis Jordan.

During the '50s, Collette performed primarily on radio and television as well as in the studios where he successfully fought racial discrimination by integrating the black and white Musicians' Unions. In 1955, he began to attract attention for his flute playing as a member of the Chico Hamilton Quintet and, along with Sam Most and Herbie Mann, helped to establish the cool-jazz style.

In addition to his ability as a multi-instrumentalist, Collette is also a composer and arranger and spent much of the '60s composing for film and arranging for Thelonious Monk. He continued to pursue composition and performing throughout the '70s and helped to found the record company, Legend, of which he became president in 1975. In the '80s, he received awards from the National Academy of Recording and Sciences (NARAS) for his performances on flute, clarinet and saxophone.

Room With Skies is on the opposite end of the spectrum from Dolphy's atonalism and angularity. Like Paul Horn's *Dida*, this solo is primarily inside and linear. Collette uses chromatic passing tones and doubling timing (16th notes) to lend contrast to the solo. Here are some examples from *Room With Skies:*

Chromatic passing tones:

Double timing:

Room With Skies

Buddy Collette

ATJ307

Eric Dolpy
SOUTH STREET EXIT

Eric Dolphy was born in Los Angeles on June 20, 1928 and died in Berlin on June 29, 1964. His first instrument was the clarinet, which he began studying at the age of eight. His ability on the clarinet was recognized early, and while still in junior high (where he also studied oboe and alto sax), he won a two year scholarship to study at the University of Southern California School of Music. After graduating high school, he continued his music studies at Los Angeles City College. In 1950, Dolphy went into the Army, and shortly thereafter joined the U.S. Naval School of Music in Washington, D.C., where he received his certificate in 1952.

Dolphy returned to Los Angeles to pursue the career of professional musician where he worked with George Brown, Eddie Beal, Gerald Wilson and Buddy Collette. Upon the recommendation of Collette, Dolphy left Los Angeles in the late '50s to join Chico Hamilton's Quintet. It was as a member of the Quintet that Dolphy's earliest recorded flute work appears. In 1960, Dolphy left Hamilton to play with Charles Mingus' group, where he began to receive recognition on a larger scale.

Like many jazz people of his generation, Dolphy was strongly influenced by alto saxophonist Charlie Parker. His other influences were Ornette Coleman, Thelonious Monk and John Coltrane, as well as 20th Century composers Edgard Varese and Gunther Schuller. A multi-instrumentalist of the highest caliber, Dolphy displayed astonishing virtuosity on the alto saxophone, flute and bass clarinet, and received critical acclaim on all of these instruments. He won the Down Beat Critics' Poll ("New Star" category) in 1961 on alto saxophone, in 1962 on flute and in 1963 on bass clarinet.

Among Dolphy's many contributions to modern jazz (such as championing the bass clarinet as a legitimate jazz instrument), he was also a key figure in helping to promote the timbral possibilities of the flute. His use of such extended techniques as multiphonics (fingerings that produce two or more tones simultaneously) and whistle-tones in his solos, significantly expanded the vocabulary of jazz flute. His playing is generally associated with the avant garde in jazz and uses elements characteristic of that style. The following are some examples taken from *South Street Exit*:

Wide leaps:

Use of fourths:

Harmonics:

Notes dissonant to the chord (atonality):

Rhythmic complexity:

ATJ307

South Street Exit

Eric Dolphy

*∘ = Harmonics
** Fingerings for high D♭ = ; for high D♮ =

ATJ307

ATJ307

Joe Farrell
SPAIN

Joe Farrell was born in Chicago Heights, Illinois on December 16, 1937 to a musical family and died in Los Angeles on January 10, 1986. He took up the clarinet at the age of eleven, inspired by a stack of Benny Goodman records. By 16, Farrell was playing tenor saxophone in Chicago. He was influenced by Charlie Parker, John Coltrane, Sonny Rollins and Stan Getz, the latter being particularly important to Farrell for his cool-jazz style. He received his degree in Music Education in 1959 from the University of Illinois.

Farrell moved to New York where he worked with musicians such as Maynard Ferguson and Slide Hampton and spent three years with the Thad Jones-Mel Lewis band. He was a first-rate studio musician and went on to make many recordings with both jazz and pop musicians. However, he is probably best known for his work during the early '70s with Chick Corea and Corea's group, Return To Forever.

Spain is one of Farrell's finest flute solos and was recorded while he was with Return To Forever. His style illustrates how the tasteful use of chromaticism can maintain interest in a solo. Notice how he uses the descending chromatic scale to create tension and ambiguity:

Another favorite device of Farrell's was the use of arpeggios. Sometimes diatonic and simple:

at other times, the arpeggios are transformed or disguised. Here, for example, by using grace notes and syncopation:

His playing was at times motivic. For example, here's the motive early in the solo:

and here it is again later, though this time transposed and altered to fit a different harmony:

ATJ307

Spain
Chick Corea

* Generally, harmonics are produced by overblowing a lower note– usually a fifth below the harmonic, i.e. overblown F = C̊.

14

DIDA

Aptly-named Paul Horn was born in New York on March 17, 1930. He began studying the piano at age four, and took up the saxophone at age twelve. In 1952, he studied flute at Oberlin College Conservatory, and in 1953 received his Masters Degree in Music from the Manhattan School of Music. He too is an alumnus of the Chico Hamilton Quintet, with whom he played from 1956 - '58.

During his prolific career, Horn has performed as a tenor saxophonist, clarinetist, flutist and composer in a wide array of musical settings ranging from the film studios of Hollywood to recording solo flute improvisations inside both the Great Pyramids of Cheops in Egypt and the Taj Mahal in India. He's been seen on screen as well as in television and motion pictures. He toured extensively, including a 1979 tour of China and a 1983 tour of the Soviet Union. In addition, Horn is known as a forerunner in the use of electronic effects.

Horn has made numerous recordings and since 1981 managed his own record company, Golden Flute, where he has been an active participant in the recording of New Age music. He is an accomplished flutist who possesses both a solid technique and a good musical mind. His playing might be described as "thoughtful" or "cool" and his recordings are well-balanced efforts.

Dida is a fine example of Horn's lyrical style. The solo is primarily "inside" (i.e., it doesn't utilize too many notes dissonant to the chords) and has a clear sense of direction. Other characteristics of this solo include the following:

Rhythmic motives:

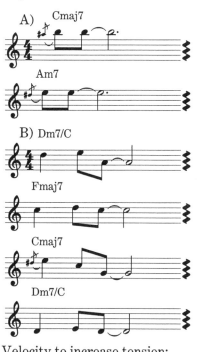

Velocity to increase tension:

Chromaticism:

Dida

Joan Baez

Hubert Laws was born to a musical family (his brother is Ronnie Laws) in Houston, Texas on November 10, 1939. He spent his teenage years playing flute both in a jazz sextet and with the Houston Youth Symphony. He received a scholarship to the Julliard School of Music and while there played with the Berkshire Festival Orchestra and the Orchestra, USA. Before turning exclusively to flute, Laws also played tenor saxophone and made recordings with artists such as Mongo Santamaria, Lena Horne and Sergio Mendez.

Laws also worked as a studio musician, played flute for television commercials and Broadway shows and as a substitute for the New York Philharmonic and the Metropolitan Opera Orchestra. While a member of the David Frost Show Band, he secured a recording contract with CTI records which proved to be a turning point in his career. He made several recordings as a leader and appeared frequently as a sideman.

During the '70s, Laws was widely celebrated and was one of the few jazz musicians to consistently play concert halls. In addition to performance of jazz, pop and gospel numbers, Laws' groups played modified versions of classical masterpieces such as Bach's *Passacaglia in C Minor* and a version of Stravinsky's *The Rite of Spring* that had been arranged to include improvised sections. He is also one of a few to successfully play piccolo in jazz and is strongly identified with that instrument. However, as a flutist, Laws possesses an extraordinary technique (from impeccable intonation to circular breathing), and his virtuosity helped to set new standards for jazz flutists in addition to helping popularize the instrument.

Airegin (Nigeria spelled backwards) was composed by Sonny Rollins and is one of Laws' most enduring solos. There is no chordal instrument present in this rendition, just flute and drums (Steve Gadd), so the chord symbols provided are those normally associated with the composition. The solo is long and demonstrates not only remarkable physical stamina, but great be-bop playing as well.

Notice how Laws adjusts the four-note ascending pattern to meet the changing harmonies:

Laws' style is abundant in the use of scales:

and rhythmic motives:

These devices help to make Laws' solos coherent and lyrical.

Airegin
Sonny Rollins

ATJ307

* Note that Laws jumps to first ending (12 measures)
  instead of playing the 2nd (8 measures).
** Fingering for harmonic E♭ is the same as overblown A♭:

ATJ307

BEAUTIFUL LOVE

Herbie Mann was born in New York City on April 16, 1930. He began studying clarinet at the age of nine, and later learned the flute and saxophone. His musical experience has been long and varied, as well as diverse stylistically. Mann's musical horizons are not strictly limited to jazz; he's recorded music indigenous to other cultures, such as Brazilian music and Japanese court music.

During the '50s, Mann played and recorded with Mat Mathews and Pete Rugolo, toured France and Scandinavia, and then formed his own sextet combining jazz and African music. Early in 1960, the group toured 15 African countries. Throughout the decade Mann continued to tour and record extensively, his familiarity with Brazilian music evolving from two tours (1961/1963) there. The '70s found Mann recording and producing several albums (including some ventures into rock) that charted, and he had a hit on the pop singles chart with his recording *Hijack* (1975). In 1981, he started his own record company, Herbie Mann Music.

Of all the jazz flutists, Mann is probably the most commercially successfully, since so many of his albums have been best sellers. Popular throughout his career, Mann dominated the Down Beat Readers' Poll for Best Flutist for 13 consecutive years (1957 - 1971).

Mann's solo on *Beautiful Love* is a fine example of linear and motivic improvisation. Throughout the solo, motivic sequences and scale fragments abound. In addition to providing structural integrity, these devices help give Mann's solo a highly melodic and lyrical quality.

Motivic sequence and variation:

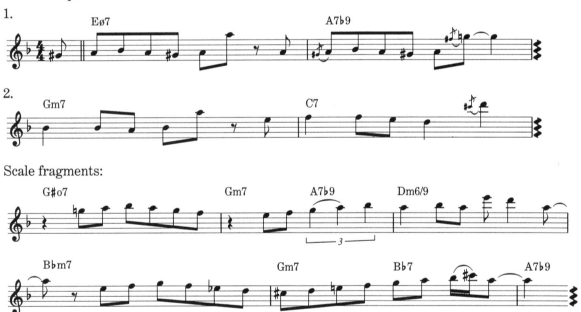

Scale fragments:

ATJ307

Beautiful Love

Haven Gillespie, Victor Young, Wayne King,
and Egbert Anson Van Alstyne

* Originally performed on alto flute, this transcription transposes all pitches up an octave.

ATJ307

James Moody was born in Savannah, Georgia on February 26, 1925. He didn't begin studying alto saxophone until he was 16, and later learned tenor saxophone and flute. In 1946, Moody made his debut with Dizzy Gillespie's big band playing tenor sax. He remained both a close personal friend and frequent musical companion of the legendary trumpeter and was back with Gillespie's group in '63 as well.

During his long career, Moody has performed and recorded (both as a leader and a sideman) in a wide variety of contexts and a wide area of geography (he spent a long time working in Europe). He has worked with such jazz giants as Milt Jackson, Al Haig, Howard McGhee and Tadd Dameron. On the international festival circuit in the '80s, Moody delighted audiences with his tenor battles with Johnny Griffin.

For over forty years, Moody has received critical acclaim for his work as a multi-instrumentalist and composer (among others, vocalists King Pleasure and Eddie Jefferson have recorded Moody's tunes). He possesses an extraordinary technique on saxophones and flute, and is generally recognized as one of the finest doublers of his generation. In fact, his flute sound has been noted to be "fleet and sweet."

Feelin' Low is a fine example of Moody's flute playing and shows why Moody has been considered as one of the top jazz flutists for so many years. Here are some examples:

Use of triads:

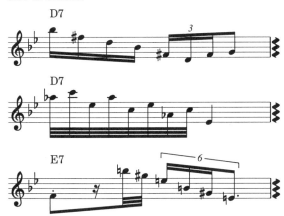

Melodic motive:

transposed:

Rhythmic complexity

Feelin' Low
James Moody

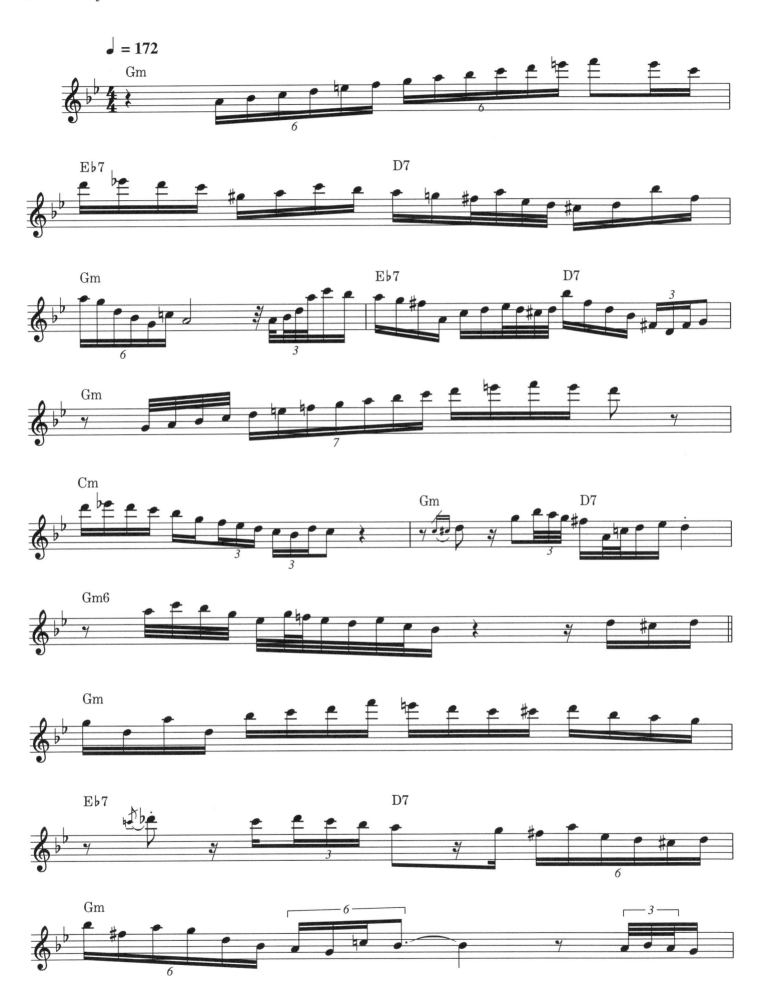

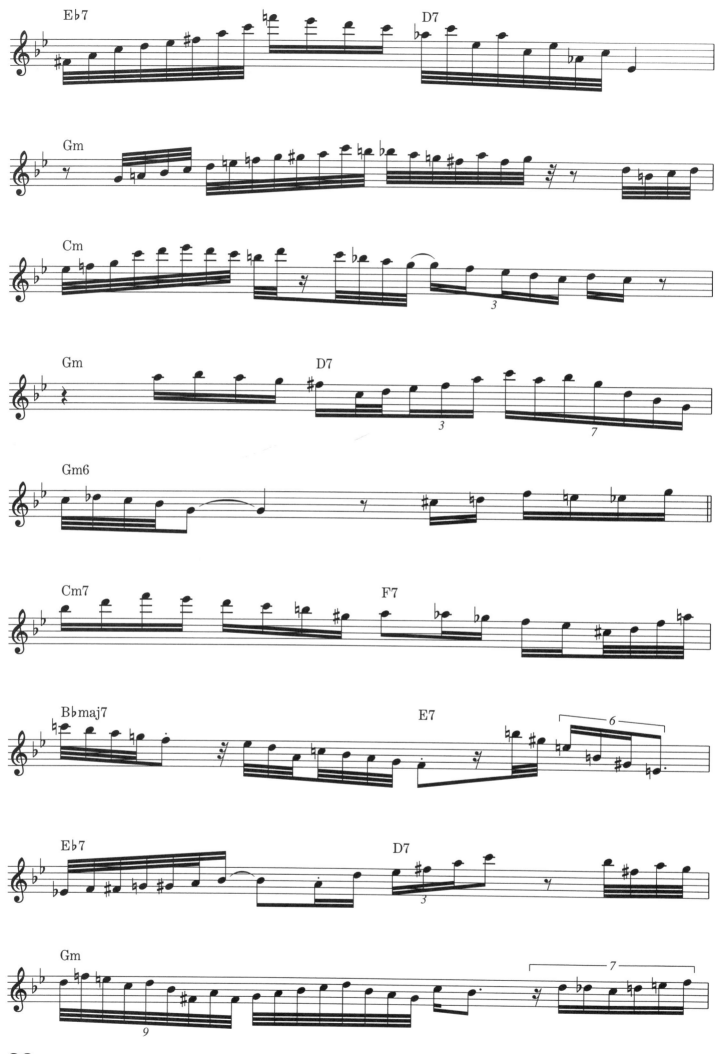

32

Sam Most
THE EYES HAVE IT

Sam Most was born in Atlantic City, New Jersey on December 16, 1930 and comes from a musical family (his brother is clarinetist Abe Most). Before turning exclusively to the flute, Most worked as a multi-instrumentalist, playing alto saxophone, clarinet and flute with Tommy Dorsey (1949), Boyd Raeburn and Don Redman. He found that the flute was best suited for his musical needs and in 1953 made his first recording, *Undercurrent Blues*. This record helped to establish Most as a pioneer of jazz flute, particularly in be-bop. He continued to lead successful groups throughout the 1950s and was one of the earliest in jazz to incorporate the technique of singing (or humming) and overblowing simultaneously along with the flute, a technique which is widely used in jazz today and is also common in rock (Ian Anderson of the group Jethro Tull). In 1954, Most won the *Down Beat* critics' "New Star" award and from 1959 to 1961 worked with Buddy Rich's orchestra, touring the Far East, India and South America. After returning to the U.S., Most spent time playing with Louie Bellson (primarily on alto saxophone) and with his brother Abe in Los Angeles. He continued working as a free-lance musician in California and playing with Red Norvo in Las Vegas. During the mid-1970s, his career attracted attention with the release of recordings for the Xanadu label. Most has continued to remain an influential voice in jazz flute and has also published a book of patterns to assist the jazz flutist.

The Eyes Have It is based on the chord progression of the standard tune, *The Night Has a Thousand Eyes*. This practice of borrowing the progression from one tune to compose another was not uncommon in the be-bop era. Be-boppers loved the progressions of the "old" standards as vehicles for their solos, but not necessarily the original tempos or melodies. For example, the Tadd Dameron tune *Hot House* (frequently performed by Charlie Parker and Dizzy Gillespie) is a sophisticated melody composed over the changes to the standard tune *What Is This Thing Called Love?* This solo uses a variety of devices, including the following:

D major pentatonic scale:

Use of rhythmic accents:

Motivic playing:

variation, transposed down a step:

the G Blues scale:

The Eyes Have It

Sam Most

* Based on the chords of *The Night Has a Thousand Eyes*.

ATJ307

James Newton
RICHMOND IN ACROPOLIS

James Newton was born in Los Angeles on May 1, 1953. He began learning the flute at the age of 17 after initially gaining musical experience playing other instruments such as the electric bass and alto and tenor saxophones. Later he studied flute with Buddy Collette and Jimmy Walker (former principal flutist of the Los Angeles Philharmonic). A remarkably fast learner, Newton quickly established a reputation as one of the premier jazz flutists in the world and since 1982 has consistently placed first as the best jazz flutist in both the *Down Beat* Critic's Poll and the *Down Beat* Readers' Poll (the latter starting in 1983).

As a flutist, Newton possesses a superb command of the instrument. His tremendous facility in the high register coupled with his unique singing/playing style and large vocabulary of extended techniques (such as multiphonics) have helped to substantially broaden the public's awareness of the flute's expressive possibilities.

In addition to his many achievements on the flute, Newton's recordings have also earned critical acclaim. For example, in 1983, *The James Newton Album* won the prestigious Montreux Grand Prix du Disc award, and in 1986, *The African Flower* won the *Down Beat* Critic's award for best album of the year.

Newton's musical influences include Eric Dolphy, John Coltrane, Duke Ellington, Charles Mingus and Jimi Hendrix as well as classical composers Maurice Ravel and Alban Berg. As an improvisor, Newton is particularly skilled in using rhythmic complexity and chromaticism in his solos, such as in the following examples from *Richmond In Acropolis:*

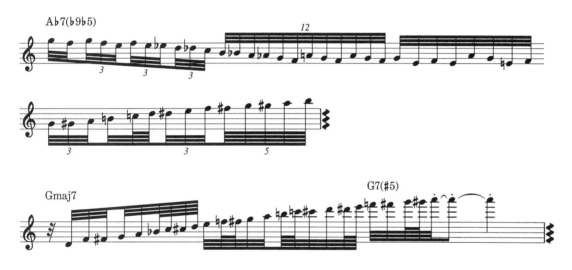

Richmond in Acropolis

James Newton

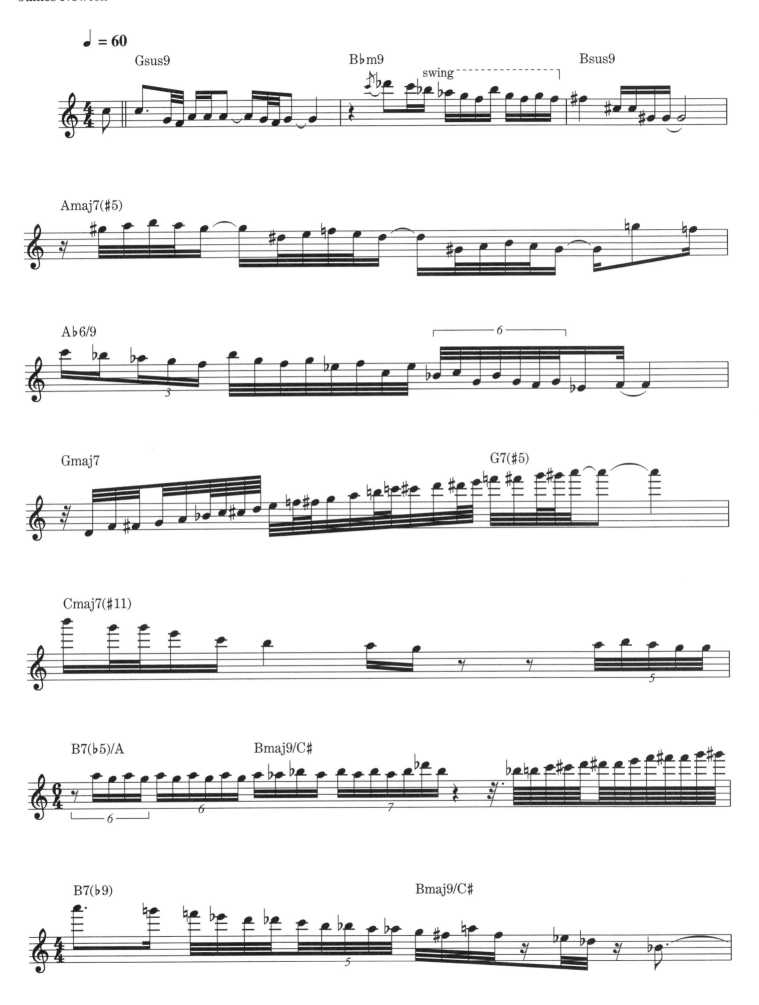

Bb7(b5)/C

G7(#9)/B

Bbmaj7(#5)

Am(#7)　　　　　　　　　　　　**A7(#5)**

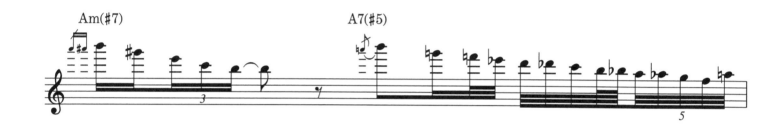

Ab7(b9b5)

Amaj7(#5)　　　　　　　　　　　**A6/9**

Abmaj9/Bb

ATJ307

Jeremy Steig
OLEO

Jeremy Steig was born in New York on September 23, 1943. His first instrument was the recorder which he began when he was 6. At the age of 11, he started studying the flute and by the time he was 15, he was playing professionally. At the age of 20, Steig recorded his debut album as a leader, *Flute Fever* (1963) with Denny Zeitlin on piano. Despite his young age, Flute Fever showed Steig as a mature and formidable improvisor, highly capable of negotiating demanding material such as *Oleo*, the album's first selection.

In 1967, Steig formed the jazz-rock group Jeremy and the Satyrs. This group used modal-oriented compositions and featured Steig employing such extended techniques as multiphonics and electronic effects such as the wah-wah pedal. In 1969, pianist Bill Evans featured Steig as soloist with his trio for an album called *What's New?*. Evans, who had played flute while in the Army, was a big fan of Steig's originality and devoted much of the album's liner notes in praise of Steig. Steig has also performed and recorded with bassist Eddie Gomez on several occasions and, in 1980, recorded the album *Rain Forest* with Gomez.

As a flutist, Steig's mastery of the technique of simultaneously singing and playing the flute is perhaps his most distinguishing feature and an integral part of his style. On *Oleo* (a Sonny Rollins composition based on the chord progression to the standard tune *I Got Rhythm*), Steig starts his solo by using the typical flute tone for the first two choruses. The rest of the solo features Steig's remarkable command of the singing (overblowing) technique. Other elements characteristic of Steig's style include the following:

Chromaticism:

Motivic development:

Syncopation:

Oleo
Sonny Rollins

* Harmonic fingering for high E♮ is the same as overblown A♮ ; for high C♮ =

ATJ307

ATJ307

*See footnote re harmonics on page 14.

*Note this extra A section.

ATJ307

Dave Valentin
FOOTPRINTS (I)
FOOTPRINTS (II)

Dave Valentin was born on April 29, 1952 in the South Bronx of New York. He had an unusually rich musical upbringing, which was partially due to the influence of his father (a merchant marine who made a point of bringing home records and instruments from places such as Brazil and Venezuela) and the musical climate which exists in the Bronx. He began studying the flute at the age of 18. Until then, Valentin had been an aspiring percussionist and was attending the High School of Music and Art in Manhattan as a percussion major. He learned quickly, and soon after starting the flute, began studying it seriously with such established flutists as Hubert Laws and Herbie Mann. His break as a soloist came when he was signed by producers Dave Grusin and Larry Rosen as one of the first artists for the GRP label. Valentin's first album for GRP was *Legends*, which was released in 1978. He has since made many recordings for GRP that have received both impressive reviews and sales, helping to establish Valentin as one of the most influential flutists of the '80s. In 1985, Valentin received a Grammy nomination for best R & B Instrumental for his version of Stevie Wonder's composition, *Love Light in Flight*, and in 1988 and 1989 was voted as the No. 1 flutist in the people's poll of Jazz Is magazine.

The next two transcriptions are of Wayne Shorter's minor blues, *Footprints*. Both versions were recorded by Valentin; the first from his album *Flute Juice* and the second from his album *Live at the Blue Note*. It is interesting to compare the two versions for similarities and differences, as well as to observe the changes in mood and intensity that exist between the studio and live recording. The two solos also show an axiom of jazz in use: good improvisors never play the same solo twice.

Perhaps the most distinctive characteristics of Valentin's flute playing are his use of rhythm and repetition. Some of the most exciting moments in his music are rhythmically- or repetitively-based, such as in the following examples taken from his solo on *Live at the Blue Note:*

Repetition:

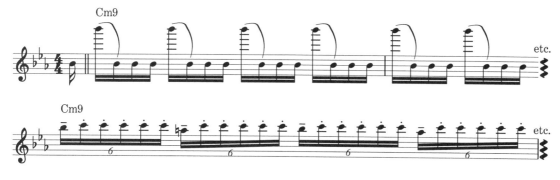

Sequences:

Motivic playing:

Syncopation:

Pentatonics: A 5 note scale (not major or minor form of pentatonic scale)

Footprints (I)

Wayne Shorter

ATJ307

Footprints (II)

Wayne Shorter

ATJ307

CATALOGUE OF PHRASES
ON V-I AND ii-V-I PROGRESSIONS

1

a. *Collette*

b. *Laws*

2

a. *Moody*

b. *Moody*

c. *Moody*

d. *Most*

e. *Most*

3

a.

4

a.

5

a.

b.

6

a.

b.

c.

d.

Laws

e.

Steig

f.

Steig

g.

Steig

7

a.

Collette

8

a.

Laws

b.

Laws

9

a.

Laws

DISCOGRAPHY

BUDDY COLLETTE	Room With Skies	Buddy Collette with Quintetto Basso-Valdambrini *LP: Family SFR-RI 625*
ERIC DOLPHY	South Street Exit	Last Date *CD: Fontana 822 226-2*
JOE FARRELL	Spain	Chick Corea - Light As A Feather *LP: Polydor PD 5525*
PAUL HORN	Dida	Visions *LP: Epic KE 32837*
HUBERT LAWS	Airegin	In The Beginning *LP: CTI-P1098*
HERBIE MANN	Beautiful Love	When Lights Are Low *LP: Portrait Masters RJ 44095*
JAMES MOODY	Feelin' Low	The Blues And Other Colors *LP: Milestone MSP 9023*
SAM MOST	The Eyes Have It	But Beautiful *LP: Catalyst CAT-7609*
JAMES NEWTON	Richmond In Acropolis	James Newton Quartet *CD: Jazz Line/Delta 11 124*
JEREMY STEIG	Oleo	Flute Fever *LP: Columbia CS8964*
DAVE VALENTIN	Footprints (I) (studio) Footprints (II) (live)	Flute Juice *LP: GRP-A-1004* Live At The Blue Note *CD: GRP/GRD-9568*